SATs Made Simple
Multiplication and Division
Ages 10-11

Partitioning Share

Times table

Product

Grid method ✕

$43\overline{)645}$

$\frac{1}{3}$ Multiples

6, 12, 18 Divide

Mixed operations

Groups

✕	20	3
5		

➗

Array

Remainder

Multiply Fractions

SCHOLASTIC

Published in the UK by Scholastic Education, 2021
Book End, Range Road, Witney, Oxfordshire, OX29 0YD
A division of Scholastic Limited
London – New York – Toronto – Sydney – Auckland
Mexico City – New Delhi – Hong Kong

© 2021 Scholastic Limited

1 2 3 4 5 6 7 8 9   1 2 3 4 5 6 7 8 9 0

A British Library Cataloguing-in-Publication Data
A catalogue record for this book is available from the British Library.

ISBN 978-1407-18400-5
Printed and bound by Ashford Colour Press

Papers used by Scholastic Limited are made from wood grown in sustainable forests.

Author
Paul Hollin

Editorial team
Robin Hunt, Kate Baxter, Tracy Kewley,
David and Jackie Link

Design team
Dipa Mistry, QBS Learning

Illustration
QBS Learning

Contents

The answers can be found online at: **www.scholastic.co.uk/sats-multiplication**

How to use this book

This book provides you with a step-by-step guide to all aspects of multiplication and division for older primary-age children, providing a complete route to mastery of this essential area of the National Curriculum for mathematics at Key Stage 2.

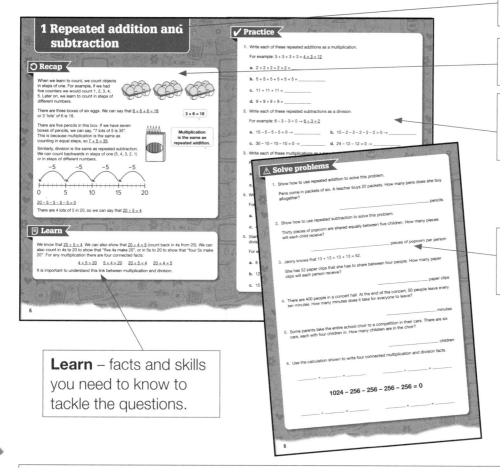

Title – there are 13 units in total and two practice tests

Recap – review what you should have learned already

Practice – practise what you have learned with arithmetic-style questions.

Solve problems – these will be similar to those you may get in your SATs test.

Learn – facts and skills you need to know to tackle the questions.

You will need multiplication and division skills for questions in all three of the KS2 mathematics SATs papers (remember, there is one Arithmetic paper and two Reasoning papers). Facts and skills from all of Key Stage 2 are tested. The more fluent your maths skills are, the more chance you have of answering questions correctly and finishing the tests in the time allowed.

At the end of the book are two practice tests which provide questions similar to those you may get in your SATs tests.

A handy progress chart on page 5 allows you to track your understanding. It is a good idea to tick off a section only when all of the questions have been completed correctly, with mistakes corrected and any misunderstandings clarified.

The answers can be found online at: **www.scholastic.co.uk/sats-multiplication**

Making progress? Tick (✔) the circles as you complete each unit of the book.

Work through one unit at a time before moving on to the next one.

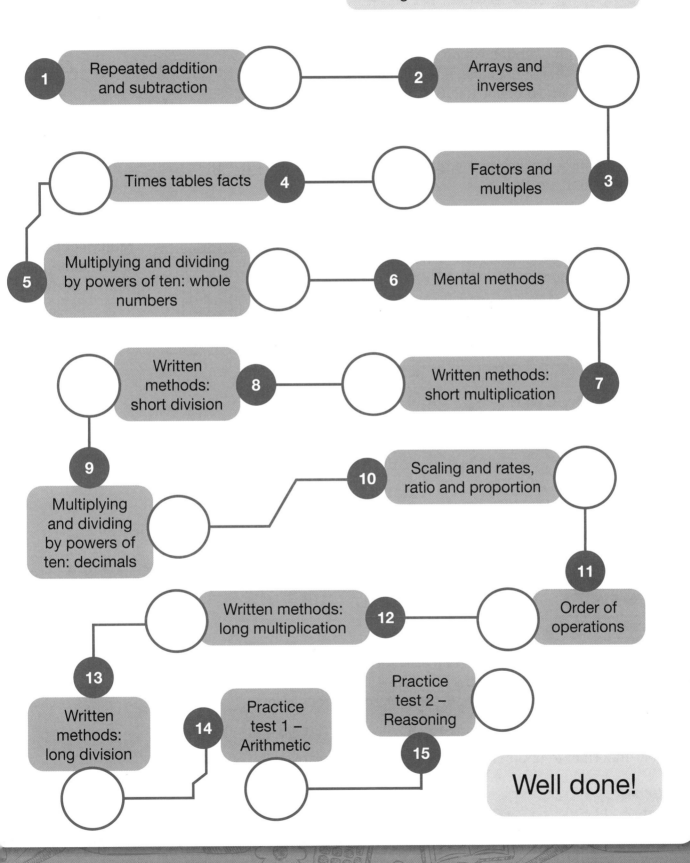

1 Repeated addition and subtraction

2 Arrays and inverses

3 Factors and multiples

4 Times tables facts

5 Multiplying and dividing by powers of ten: whole numbers

6 Mental methods

7 Written methods: short multiplication

8 Written methods: short division

9 Multiplying and dividing by powers of ten: decimals

10 Scaling and rates, ratio and proportion

11 Order of operations

12 Written methods: long multiplication

13 Written methods: long division

14 Practice test 1 – Arithmetic

15 Practice test 2 – Reasoning

Well done!

1 Repeated addition and subtraction

↻ Recap

When we learn to count, we count objects in steps of one. For example, if we had five counters we would count 1, 2, 3, 4, 5. Later on, we learn to count in steps of different numbers.

There are three boxes of six eggs. We can say that $6 + 6 + 6 = 18$ or 3 'lots' of 6 are 18.

$3 \times 6 = 18$

There are five pencils in this box. If we have seven boxes of pencils, we can say, "7 lots of 5 are 35". This is because multiplication is the same as counting in equal steps, so $7 \times 5 = 35$.

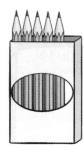

Multiplication is the same as repeated addition.

Similarly, division is the same as repeated subtraction. We can count backwards in steps of one (5, 4, 3, 2, 1) or in steps of different numbers.

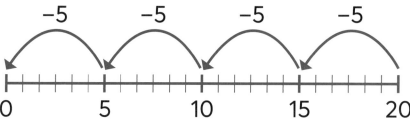

$20 - 5 - 5 - 5 - 5 = 0$

There are 4 lots of 5 in 20, so we can say that $20 \div 5 = 4$.

📄 Learn

We know that $20 \div 5 = 4$. We can also show that $20 \div 4 = 5$ (count back in 4s from 20). We can also count in 4s to 20 to show that "five 4s make 20", or in 5s to 20 to show that "four 5s make 20". For any multiplication there are four connected facts:

$$4 \times 5 = 20 \qquad 5 \times 4 = 20 \qquad 20 \div 5 = 4 \qquad 20 \div 4 = 5$$

It is important to understand this link between multiplication and division.

Practice

1. Write each of these repeated additions as a multiplication.

   For example: $3 + 3 + 3 + 3 = \underline{4 \times 3 = 12}$

   a. $2 + 2 + 2 + 2 + 2 =$ _____

   b. $5 + 5 + 5 + 5 + 5 + 5 =$ _____

   c. $11 + 11 + 11 =$ _____

   d. $9 + 9 + 9 + 9 =$ _____

2. Write each of these repeated subtractions as a division.

   For example: $6 - 3 - 3 = 0 \rightarrow \underline{6 \div 3 = 2}$

   a. $15 - 5 - 5 - 5 = 0 \rightarrow$ _____   **b.** $10 - 2 - 2 - 2 - 2 - 2 = 0 \rightarrow$ _____

   c. $30 - 10 - 10 - 10 = 0 \rightarrow$ _____   **d.** $24 - 12 - 12 = 0 \rightarrow$ _____

3. Write each of these multiplications as a repeated addition.

   For example: $3 \times 12 = 36 \rightarrow \underline{12 + 12 + 12 = 36}$

   a. $5 \times 4 = 20 \rightarrow$ _____   **b.** $3 \times 8 = 24 \rightarrow$ _____

   c. $4 \times 7 = 28 \rightarrow$ _____   **d.** $2 \times 19 = 38 \rightarrow$ _____

4. Write each of these divisions as a repeated subtraction.

   For example: $36 \div 12 = 3 \rightarrow \underline{36 - 12 - 12 - 12 = 0}$

   a. $8 \div 4 = 2 \rightarrow$ _____   **b.** $20 \div 5 = 4 \rightarrow$ _____

   c. $44 \div 11 = 4 \rightarrow$ _____   **d.** $45 \div 9 = 5 \rightarrow$ _____

5. Starting with the repeated addition shown, write four connected multiplication and division calculations.

   For example: $9 + 9 + 9 = 27 \rightarrow \underline{3 \times 9 = 27}$ $\underline{9 \times 3 = 27}$ $\underline{27 \div 9 = 3}$ $\underline{27 \div 3 = 9}$

   a. $8 + 8 + 8 + 8 + 8 = 40 \rightarrow$ _____ _____ _____ _____

   b. $12 + 12 + 12 + 12 = 48 \rightarrow$ _____ _____ _____ _____

   c. $15 + 15 + 15 = 45 \rightarrow$ _____ _____ _____ _____

⚠ Solve problems

1. Show how to use repeated addition to solve this problem.

   Pens come in packets of six. A teacher buys 20 packets. How many pens does she buy altogether?

    pens

2. Show how to use repeated subtraction to solve this problem.

   Thirty pieces of popcorn are shared equally between five children. How many pieces will each child receive?

    pieces of popcorn per person

3. Jenny knows that 13 + 13 + 13 + 13 = 52.

   She has 52 paper clips that she has to share between four people. How many paper clips will each person receive?

    paper clips

4. There are 400 people in a concert hall. At the end of the concert, every ten minutes, 50 people leave. How many minutes does it take for everyone to leave?

    minutes

5. Some parents take the entire school choir to a competition in their cars. There are six cars, each with four children in. How many children are in the choir?

   _____ children

6. Use the calculation shown to write four connected multiplication and division facts.

   $$\boxed{} \times \boxed{} = \boxed{} \qquad \boxed{} \div \boxed{} = \boxed{}$$

   ## 1024 − 256 − 256 − 256 − 256 = 0

   $$\boxed{} \div \boxed{} = \boxed{} \qquad \boxed{} \times \boxed{} = \boxed{}$$

2 Arrays and inverses

Recap

When we organise objects or pictures in a grid of columns and rows, we call it an array. An array can make calculations easier.

Three rows, of four apples tell us that 3 lots of 4 equal 12.

Or, four columns of three apples tell us that 4 lots of 3 equal 12.

This array of dots has nine columns and five rows.

There is no need to count the dots.

9 lots of 5 equal 45.

And 5 lots of 9 are also 45.

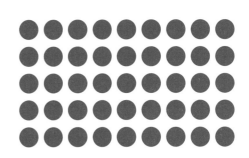

Learn

When numbers are added together the order isn't important.

6 + 7 = 13   and   7 + 6 = 13

It's the same for multiplication – the numbers can be written in any order.

> We call this the commutative law.

3 × 5 = 15   and   5 × 3 = 15

This is also true for three or more numbers. Try multiplying the numbers 2, 3 and 4 in different orders. The answer will always be 24.

When subtracting, the order is important.

It's the same for division – and there is a connection to multiplication.

3 × 4 = 12   so   12 ÷ 3 = 4

4 × 3 = 12   so   12 ÷ 4 = 3

> Inverses are very useful for mental maths and problem solving.

This is because multiplication and division are **inverses**.

1. Draw dots to show four different arrays that can be made with 12 counters.

2. Tom has six counters. Write two different arrays he can make.

   ☐ by ☐ counters and ☐ by ☐ counters

3. Gina has 24 cubes. Write six different arrays she can make.

   ☐ by ☐ cubes   ☐ by ☐ cubes   ☐ by ☐ cubes

   ☐ by ☐ cubes   ☐ by ☐ cubes   ☐ by ☐ cubes

4. This array has ten rows of 12 dots.

   a. How many dots are there altogether? _____

   b. Write two multiplication and two division facts using the array.

   ☐ × ☐ = ☐   ☐ ÷ ☐ = ☐

   ☐ ÷ ☐ = ☐   ☐ × ☐ = ☐

5. Draw lines to connect each multiplication fact to its inverse.

   | 12 × 7 = 84 | | 48 ÷ 4 = 12 |

   | 8 × 9 = 72 | | 84 ÷ 7 = 12 |

   | 4 × 12 = 48 | | 72 ÷ 9 = 8 |

   | 7 × 8 = 56 | | 56 ÷ 7 = 8 |

⚠ Solve problems

1. A teacher wants to buy some new plants for the school garden.

   The plants are packed in boxes in arrays of three rows of four.

   The teacher wants 60 plants. How many boxes does she need to buy?

   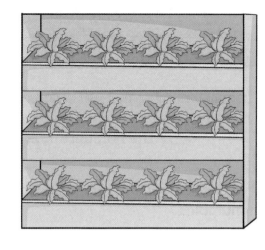

   _____ boxes

2. Yousef has 20 counters. He uses **some** of them to make an array where the number of rows equals the number of columns. Write two possible arrays he could make.

   [   ] × [   ]   and   [   ] × [   ]

3. A farmer grows cabbages in rows. There are eight rows with 12 cabbages in each row, and three rows with ten cabbages in each row.

   How many cabbages are there altogether?

   _____ cabbages

4. A teacher arranges some pieces of chocolate in a seven by eight array. There are 24 children in the class. Each child has two pieces of chocolate.

   How many pieces of chocolate will be left over?

   [   ] pieces

5. A grocer arranges some egg boxes, each containing six eggs, in an array of eight by ten.

   How many eggs are there in one array?

   _____ eggs

6. A family of five wins £240 in a lottery. They want to share the money between them equally. Tom uses this calculation: £240 ÷ 5 = £48 each.

   Tom wants to check his answer using an inverse calculation. Which of these calculations should he use? Circle your answer.

   24 × 10 = 240   10 × 24 = 240   48 × 5 = 240   240 ÷ 5 = 48

3 Factors and multiples

↻ Recap

A smaller number that will divide exactly into a larger number is called a **factor**.

> **The numbers 1, 2, 3, 4, 6 and 12 are all factors of 12.**

A larger number that is made by multiplying a smaller number by another number is called a **multiple**.

> **12 is a multiple of 4.**

> **In fact, 12 is a multiple of six different numbers: 1, 2, 3, 4, 6 and 12.**

📑 Learn

Factor pairs: Two numbers that multiply together to make a larger number are called a factor pair.

> **1×12, 2×6 and 3×4 are all factor pairs of 12.**

Common factors: Some numbers have one or more factors in common. For example, 4 is a common factor of 8 and 12, and 5 is a common factor of 15 and 20.

Highest common factors: To find the highest common factor of two numbers, list all the factors of each number. The factors of 10 are 1, 2, 5 and 10. The factors of 15 are 1, 3, 5 and 15.

> **So the highest common factor of 10 and 15 is 5.**

Common multiples: We call two numbers that share a factor common multiples of that number. For example, 30 and 50 are common multiples of 10.

Prime numbers: These can only be divided by themselves and 1. The first five prime numbers are 2, 3, 5, 7 and 11.

> **A factor that is a prime number is called a prime factor.**

Square numbers: A square number is the result of multiplying a number by itself. We say 'five squared' and write 5^2.

$2^2 = 2 \times 2 = 4$ $\quad$ $3^2 = 3 \times 3 = 9$ $\quad$ $5^2 = 5 \times 5 = 25$ $\quad$ $10^2 = 10 \times 10 = 100$

Cube numbers: A cube number is the result of multiplying a number by itself, and then itself again. We say 'five cubed' and write 5^3.

$5^3 = 5 \times 5 \times 5 = 125$ $\quad$ ($5 \times 5 = 25$ and $25 \times 5 = 125$)

Zero and one: Any number multiplied by 1 remains the same, and any number divided by 1 remains the same. And remember, any number multiplied by zero equals zero, and we cannot divide by zero.

1. Write all the factor pairs for each of these numbers.

   a. 6 _____

   b. 10 _____

   c. 13 _____

   d. 24 _____

   e. 35 _____

   f. 27 _____

2. Find the highest common factor for each set of numbers.

   a. 8 and 20 _____

   b. 12 and 15 _____

   c. 24 and 60 _____

   d. 25 and 50 _____

   e. 6, 18 and 30 _____

   f. 14, 21 and 35 _____

3. Write down **only** the prime factors for each number.

   a. 16 _____

   b. 12 _____

   c. 28 _____

   d. 45 _____

   e. 44 _____

   f. 25 _____

4. **a.** What is the only **even** prime number? _____

   b. Write all the prime numbers up to 20: _____

5. Calculate these squares.

   a. 5^2 = _____

   b. 2^2 = _____

   c. 10^2 = _____

   d. 3^2 = _____

   e. 7^2 = _____

   f. 4^2 = _____

   g. 1^2 = _____

   h. 6^2 = _____

   i. 11^2 = _____

6. Calculate these cubes.

   a. 2^3 = _____

   b. 3^3 = _____

   c. 10^3 = _____

   d. 1^3 = _____

   e. 0^3 = _____

   f. 4^3 = _____

   g. 5^3 = _____

   h. 6^3 = _____

   i. 11^3 = _____

⚠ Solve problems

1. Tick (✔) each statement that is true.

   a. 12 has six factors ⬜

   b. 50 is a common multiple of 4, 5 and 1 ⬜

   c. 55 has two prime factors ⬜

   d. $2^3 - 2^2 = 2^2$ ⬜

2. Write all the numbers from 1 to 12 in the correct place on the sorting diagram.

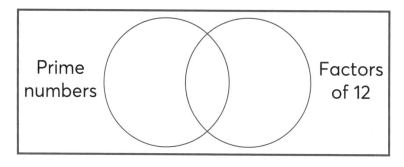

Prime numbers   Factors of 12

3. Josh says, "Ten squared minus six squared equals eight squared."

   Is Josh correct? Use calculations to explain.

   _____

   _____

4. Tina is using small wooden cubes to build larger cubes.

   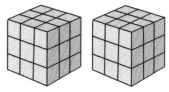

   She makes each large cube three small cubes wide, three cubes long and three cubes high.

   Tina has 100 small wooden cubes. How many bigger cubes can she build, and how many little cubes will be left over?

   Tina can make _____ large cubes. She will have _____ small wooden cubes left over.

4 Times tables facts

Recap

The times tables square can help us to learn lots of facts and skills.

We can use the square to find any multiplication fact from 1 × 1 to 12 × 12.

For example, to find 7 × 6, find the 7 on the left-hand side and the 6 along the top. Follow the row across from 7 and the column down from 6: they meet at 42. So 7 × 6 = 42.

> Use some other times tables facts to check you can use the table. For example, 3 × 5 = 15, 8 × 9 = 72, and 12 × 4 = 48.

The times tables square

	1	2	3	4	5	6	7	8	9	10	11	12
1	1	2	3	4	5	6	7	8	9	10	11	12
2	2	4	6	8	10	12	14	16	18	20	22	24
3	3	6	9	12	15	18	21	24	27	30	33	36
4	4	8	12	16	20	24	28	32	36	40	44	48
5	5	10	15	20	25	30	35	40	45	50	55	60
6	6	12	18	24	30	36	42	48	54	60	66	72
7	7	14	21	28	35	42	49	56	63	70	77	84
8	8	16	24	32	40	48	56	64	72	80	88	96
9	9	18	27	36	45	54	63	72	81	90	99	108
10	10	20	30	40	50	60	70	80	90	100	110	120
11	11	22	33	44	55	66	77	88	99	110	121	132
12	12	24	36	48	60	72	84	96	108	120	132	144

Learn

A single times tables fact can tell us many different things. Use the times tables square to check this fact:

$$3 \times 7 = 21$$

From this one fact we can also say:

- 7 × 3 = 21: because multiplications can be done either way (the commutative law).

- 21 ÷ 7 = 3: because division is the **inverse** of multiplication.

- 21 ÷ 3 = 7: also because division is the **inverse** of multiplication.

- 3 and 7 are both **factors** of 21: because a factor will divide exactly into a larger number.

- 21 is a **multiple** of 3 and 7: because a multiple comes from multiplying two numbers together. We can also say 21 is a **common multiple** of 3 and 7.

- 21 is **not** a **prime number**: because a prime number can only be divided by itself and 1.

  (Tip – the only prime numbers on the times tables square are 2, 3, 5, 7 and 11.)

- 21 is not a square number: because a square number is the result of a number multiplied by itself.

1. Insert the missing numbers.

    a. $3 \times 8 = \boxed{}$

    b. $6 \times 9 = \boxed{}$

    c. $7 \times 5 = \boxed{}$

    d. $8 \times 12 = \boxed{}$

    e. $4 \times \boxed{} = 24$

    f. $\boxed{} \times 5 = 55$

    g. $12 \times \boxed{} = 36$

    h. $\boxed{} \times \boxed{} = 49$

    i. $\boxed{} \times \boxed{} = 77$

2. Insert the missing numbers.

    a. $30 \div 5 = \boxed{}$

    b. $32 \div 4 = \boxed{}$

    c. $72 \div 8 = \boxed{}$

    d. $15 \div 3 = \boxed{}$

    e. $12 \div \boxed{} = 6$

    f. $35 \div \boxed{} = 7$

    g. $\boxed{} \div 10 = 11$

    h. $84 \div \boxed{} = 7$

    i. $\boxed{} \div 11 = 9$

3. Write all of the squared numbers on the times tables square in order.

    _____

4. Write all of the prime numbers between 1 and 100. Remember, 1 is not a prime number.

    _____

5. Write three multiples from the times tables square for each of these numbers.

    For example: 3: <u>9, 15, 27</u>

    a. 2: _____
    b. 5: _____
    c. 8: _____
    d. 12: _____

6. Circle the two **incorrect** factors in each list.

    a. Factors of 6: 1 2 3 4 5 6

    b. Factors of 18: 1 2 3 6 8 9 12 18

    c. Factors of 30: 1 2 3 4 5 6 10 12 15

    d. Factors of 17: 1 7 10 17

7. Write the common multiples from the times tables square for each pair of numbers.

    For example: 2, 3: <u>6, 12, 24</u>

    a. 3, 5: _____
    b. 2, 7: _____
    c. 5, 9: _____

⚠ Solve problems

1. Write four calculations from the times table square that use 35: two multiplications and two divisions.

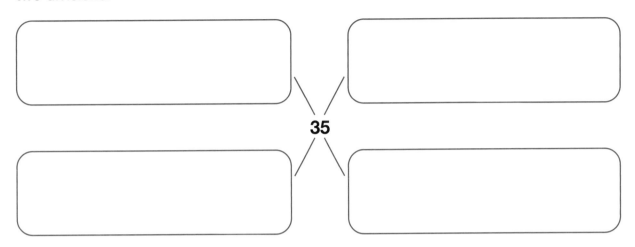

2. Ishmael says, "11 is the biggest prime number on the times tables square."

   Explain why he is right.

   _____

   _____

3. **a.** Which number appears most often on the times tables square? _____

   b. List all of its factors in order from low to high. _____

4. Carlos packs a crate with new TVs. It has a total mass of exactly 85 kilograms. Each TV has a mass of 8 kilograms. The crate itself has a mass of 13 kilograms.

   How many TVs are in the crate?

   _____ TVs

5. For a school fundraising event, children earn money by doing jobs for their neighbours. Twelve children earn £3 each, six children earn £5 each, and nine children earn £10 each.

   How much does the class raise altogether?

   £ _____

5 Multiplying and dividing by powers of ten: whole numbers

↻ Recap

Our number system uses base 10. This means that the digits represent different powers of 10 depending on their position.

> **Each column represents a power of 10.**

Powers mean squared ($10^2 = 10 \times 10 = 100$), cubed ($10^3 = 10 \times 10 \times 10 = 1000$), and so on.

Look at the number thirty-two thousand eight hundred and fifty-six.

Ten thousands	Thousands	Hundreds	Tens	Ones
$10^4 = 10,000$s	$10^3 = 1000$s	$10^2 = 100$s	$10^1 = 10$s	$10^0 = 1$s
3	2	8	5	6

We can see that the 8 digit represents 800, the 3 digit 30,000, and so on.

📄 Learn

We know from the times tables square that $10 \times 6 = 60$. When we multiply by 10, the 6 moves from the ones column to the tens column: we have **increased** it ten times (by a power of 10).

> **It works for large numbers too. For example, $825 \times 10 = 8250$, $825 \times 1000 = 825,000$.**

We move numbers one place to the left for every power of ten we multiply by. So, $100 \times 6 = 600$ and $1000 \times 6 = 6000$.

We can extend this to larger multiples, such as $12 \times 3000 = 36,000$ ($12 \times 3 = 36$ and $36 \times 1000 = 36,000$).

When we divide by a power of 10, we move every digit one place to the right. The number **decreases** by a power of 10.

We know from the times tables square that $70 \div 10 = 7$.

Similarly, $120 \div 10 = 12$. Notice how the numbers move one place to the right and the zero from the ones column is lost.

> **The same rules apply to large numbers: $2400 \div 100 = 24$, $7000 \div 10 = 700$ and $130,000 \div 10,000 = 13$.**

We can extend this to larger divisors, such as $450 \div 90 = 5$ ($450 \div 10 = 45$ and $45 \div 9 = 5$).

Similarly, $36,000 \div 3000 = 12$ ($36,000 \div 1000 = 36$ and $36 \div 3 = 12$).

1. Write these numbers using digits.

    a. Three thousand and seventy-five _____

    b. Forty-eight thousand two hundred and ninety _____

    c. One hundred thousand _____

    d. Six-hundred and fifteen thousand, one hundred and seven _____

2. Complete these multiplications.

    a. $10 \times 12 =$ [ ]

    b. $10 \times 24 =$ [ ]

    c. $10 \times 360 =$ [ ]

    d. $437 \times 10 =$ [ ]

    e. $31 \times 100 =$ [ ]

    f. $250 \times 1000 =$ [ ]

    g. $40 \times 300 =$ [ ]

    h. $50 \times 800 =$ [ ]

    i. $800 \times 900 =$ [ ]

3. Complete these divisions.

    a. $80 \div 10 =$ [ ]

    b. $120 \div 10 =$ [ ]

    c. $200 \div 10 =$ [ ]

    d. $800 \div 100 =$ [ ]

    e. $9000 \div 100 =$ [ ]

    f. $23{,}000 \div 100 =$ [ ]

    g. $500 \div 50 =$ [ ]

    h. $240 \div 40 =$ [ ]

    i. $66{,}000 \div 1100 =$ [ ]

4. Answer these mixed calculations.

    a. $42 \times 100 =$ [ ]

    b. $400 \times 500 =$ [ ]

    c. $1200 \div 300 =$ [ ]

    d. $12 \times 12{,}000 =$ [ ]

    e. $8100 \div 900 =$ [ ]

    f. $7200 \div 800 =$ [ ]

    g. $7000 \times 110 =$ [ ]

    h. $2700 \div 30 =$ [ ]

    i. $60 \times 2200 =$ [ ]

⚠ Solve problems

1. Draw a line to match each calculation to its correct answer.

   a.

700 × 600	42,000
420 × 100	4200
60 × 70	420,000
70 × 6	420

   b.

2400 ÷ 30	8
800,000 ÷ 100	80
240,000 ÷ 300	800
24,000 ÷ 3000	8000

2. On average, swallows live for four years. They fly 6000 miles to Africa and the same distance back to the UK every year!

   How far would a typical swallow fly in its lifetime?

   _____ miles

3. Fifty boxes of chocolate counters contain 10,000 chocolates altogether.

   How many are there in each box?

   _____ chocolate counters

4. A factory makes mattresses for beds. Inside each bed there are 2000 springs.

   This year, the factory wants to make 2500 mattresses. How many springs will it need altogether?

   _____ springs

5. A football squad wins a £180,000 prize. This is split equally between all the players in the squad. Each player receives £6000.

   How many players are there in the whole squad?

   _____ players

6 Mental methods

Written methods can help when calculations are too hard, but there is a lot of maths you can do in your head, mentally. Top tips for good mental maths with multiplication and division:

1. Think – try to understand the question and estimate the answer before you start.

2. Learn your times tables facts (see Unit 4, page 15).

3. Learn how to multiply and divide by powers of 10 (see Unit 5, page 18).

4. Learn a few basic rules (see below).

Learn

Look for inverse calculations.

If $12 \times 6 = 72$ then $6 \times 12 = 72$ and $72 \div 6 = 12$ and $72 \div 12 = 6$.

> With a few clever methods and a bit of thinking, you can save yourself time and energy!

More than two numbers can be multiplied one after the other, in any order.

$5 \times 4 \times 3 = 60$ $(3 \times 4 \times 5 = 12 \times 5 = 60)$

Look for powers of 10.

We can split powers of 10 to make a calculation easier.

For example, $30 \times 7 = 3 \times 10 \times 7 = 3 \times 7 \times 10 = 21 \times 10 = 210$.

Similarly, $320 \div 4 = 10 \times 32 \div 4 = 10 \times 8 = 80$.

Look for easier calculations.

We can also split numbers before multiplying or dividing.

For example, $23 \times 5 = 20 \times 5 + 3 \times 5 = 100 + 15 = 115$.

Similarly, $126 \div 6 = 120 \div 6 + 6 \div 6 = 20 + 1 = 21$.

> Remember, always try to understand the question and estimate the answer before you do your calculation.

Look for multiples near 10.

See if you can solve the calculation mentally.

$526 \times 11 = 526 \times 10 + 526 \times 1 = 5260 + 526 = 5786$

Or, $24 \times 9 = 24 \times 10 - 24 \times 1 = 240 - 24 = 216$

1. Solve these multiplications mentally.

   a. $2 \times 3 \times 4 =$ ☐

   b. $4 \times 5 \times 2 =$ ☐

   c. $7 \times 5 \times 2 =$ ☐

   d. $3 \times 70 =$ ☐

   e. $7 \times 106 =$ ☐

   f. $53 \times 11 =$ ☐

   g. $16 \times 9 =$ ☐

   h. $20 \times 35 =$ ☐

   i. $33 \times 22 =$ ☐

2. Solve these divisions mentally.

   a. $132 \div 11 =$ ☐

   b. $150 \div 3 =$ ☐

   c. $440 \div 4 =$ ☐

   d. $640 \div 8 =$ ☐

   e. $5000 \div 50 =$ ☐

   f. $186 \div 2 =$ ☐

   g. $2790 \div 9 =$ ☐

   h. $320 \div 20 =$ ☐

   i. $4000 \div 200 =$ ☐

3. Solve these questions mentally.

   a. $37 \times 2 =$ ☐

   b. $52 \times 4 =$ ☐

   c. $66 \div 3 =$ ☐

   d. $41 \times 11 =$ ☐

   e. $770 \div 7 =$ ☐

   f. $5 \times 55 =$ ☐

   g. $5 \times 34 \times 2 =$ ☐

   h. $248 \div 8 =$ ☐

   i. $87 \times 9 =$ ☐

   j. $8048 \div 4 =$ ☐

   k. $2480 \div 8 =$ ☐

   l. $645 \times 11 =$ ☐

4. Try these harder questions. Estimate the answer first; then solve them mentally.

   a. $18,027 \div 9$ Estimate: _____   Answer: _____

   b. 28×150 Estimate: _____   Answer: _____

   c. $14,400 \div 120$ Estimate: _____   Answer: _____

   d. 63×500 Estimate: _____   Answer: _____

   e. 860×499 Estimate: _____   Answer: _____

⚠ Solve problems

Solve these problems mentally – no written calculations allowed!

1. A farm has 15 times as many sheep as it has cows.

   If it has 30 cows, how many sheep are there?

   _____ sheep

2. There are 248 children in a school divided equally into 8 classrooms.

   How many children are there in each class?

   _____ children

3. 163 people each donate £5 to charity.

   How much will they raise altogether?

   £_____

4. In a running relay race there are four runners. Each runner does two laps of the track, and then hands over to the next runner until all four runners have done two laps of the track. The track is 400 metres long.

   How far do the four runners run **altogether**?

   _____ metres

5. One minute is 60 seconds.

   How many minutes is 660 seconds?

   _____ minutes

6. A lorry used for transporting cars has a maximum capacity of 48,600kg.

   If 12 identical cars have this mass in total, what is the mass of each car?

   _____kg

7. If 12 identical glasses each hold 240cl of water, and four different glasses each hold 100cl, how much water will be needed to fill them all?

   _____cl

8. In a warehouse, there are 100 cartons, each holding 60 boxes of six eggs.

   How many eggs are there altogether?

   _____ eggs

9. 750 people each pay £8 to a charity.

   How much money is given altogether?

   £_____

7 Written methods: short multiplication

↻ Recap

When you can't quite manage a mental calculation, written methods give you a sure way to get the right answer.

If in doubt, get your pencil out!

Remember that our numbers are written in base 10.

For an easy multiplication like 24 × 3, we can use base 10 columns.

	10s	1s
	2	4
×		3
	7	2
	1	

We do the calculation like this:

First multiply the **1s** → 3 × 4 = 12.

12 is one **10** and two **1s**, so write the 2 in the **1s** column, and put the 1 below the answer line in the **10s** column (this is called 'carrying').

Now multiply the **10s** → 3 × 2 **10s** = 6 **10s**.

Add on the carried **10** to make seven **10s**. Write the 7 in the **10s** column.

The answer is 72.

📄 Learn

The same method works for harder calculations, such as 6 × 235.

It is a good idea to estimate the answer first: 6 × 200 = 1200, and 6 × 35 is around 200, so the answer will be around 1400.

Now we can do our written calculation.

	1000s	100s	10s	1s
		2	3	5
×				6
	1	4	1	0
	1	2	3	

6 × 5 = 30 → write 0 in the **1s** column and carry the 3.

6 × 3 = 18, plus 3 is 21 → write 1 in the **10s** column and carry the 2.

6 × 2 = 12, plus 2 is 14 → write 4 in the **100s** column and 1 in the **1000s** column.

You can multiply any large number by a one-digit number using this method.

24

1. Use short multiplication.

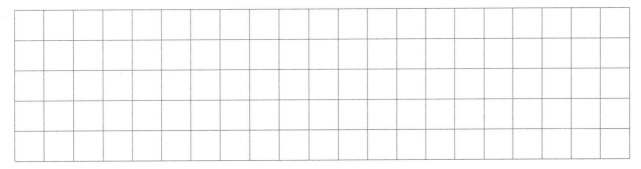

a.		10s	1s
		3	2
	×		3

b.		100s	10s	1s
			5	6
	×			2

c.		100s	10s	1s
		1	0	8
	×			4

d.		1000s	100s	10s	1s
			3	2	6
	×				5

2. Use short multiplication. Take care to lay them out correctly.

   a. 4 × 135   **b.** 5 × 256   **c.** 3 × 907   **d.** 7 × 248

3. Estimate the answer to each of these multiplications.

   a. 3 × 185 = [ ]

   b. 4 × 1273 = [ ]

   c. 8 × 317 = [ ]

   d. 5 × 2304 = [ ]

4. Now use short multiplication to complete the calculations from Question 3. Take care to lay them out correctly.

   a. 3 × 185   **b.** 4 × 1273   **c.** 8 × 317   **d.** 5 × 2304

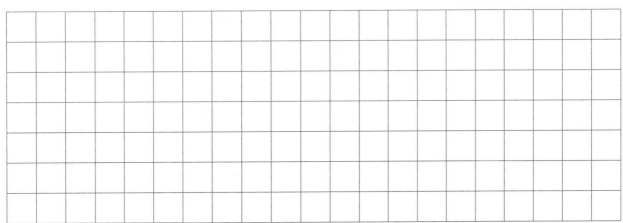

1. Write the missing digits in each multiplication.

a.

	1	□	4
×			4
	5	3	6

b.

	□	3	2
×			7
3	7	□	4

c.

	5	4	3
×		□	
2	7	1	5

d.

	2	□	7
×			3
	7	1	□

2. Eight hundred and seventy-six people each pay £5 to download a film.

   How much do they spend altogether?

   £ _____

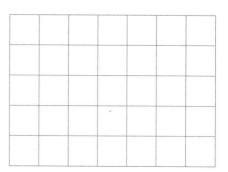

3. A school orders eight new laptops, which cost £839 each. The headteacher makes a mental estimate and says the total cost is about £6720.

   Use short multiplication to decide whether the estimate was too high or too low, and by how much.

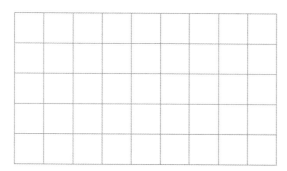

   The estimate is £_____ too high/low.

4. Seven new houses are being built. Each house is identical. The builders estimate that they need 465 roof tiles for each house. Roof tiles cost £3 each.

   Calculate how much they will spend altogether.

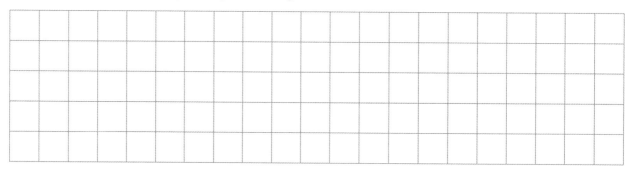

   Altogether they will spend £_____ on roof tiles.

8 Written methods: short division

Recap

We can use written methods to make division easier too.

We work out the division 471 ÷ 3 as follows.

	1	5	7
3	4	¹7	²1

We divide the 3 into each digit of 471, starting on the left, and carrying remainders forward each time.

Try doing the calculation on paper while reading through the working on the right.

- 3 divides into 4 once, remainder 1.
- The 1 is actually one **100**, so carrying this to the **10s** column makes 17 **10s**.
- 3 divides into 17 five times, remainder 2.
- The 2 is actually two **10s**, so carrying this to the **1s** column makes 21 **1s**.
- 3 divides into 21 seven times, with no remainder.

So 471 ÷ 3 = 157.

We can use short division to divide by two-digit numbers but this gets hard higher than 12.

		2	4	1
1	2	2	²8	⁴9	¹2

Can you list the working for solving this division?

Learn

Make sure you know how to deal with remainders. You might be asked to leave it as a remainder or express it as a decimal or fraction.

	1	8	5	3	r2
5	9	⁴2	²6	¹7	

Instead of a remainder we can have a decimal. Remember that the number 9267 can be written as 9267.0.

5 divides into 17 three times, with 2 left over – this gives us the r2. We can also write the remainder as a fraction, with the number we are dividing by as the denominator.

So 9267 ÷ 5 = 1853 r2 or 1853 $\frac{2}{5}$.

	1	8	5	3	•	4
5	9	⁴2	²6	¹7	•	²0

Notice that we carry the 2 over the decimal point into the $\frac{1}{10}$s column. 5 divides into 20 exactly four times. So 9267 ÷ 5 = 1853.4

Notice that $\frac{4}{10} = \frac{2}{5}$.

1. Use short division.

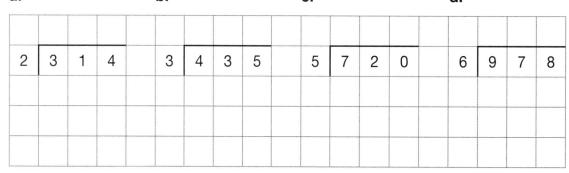

   a.　　　　　**b.**　　　　　**c.**　　　　　**d.**

2. Use short division. Take care to lay them out correctly. Give answers with remainders where necessary.

   a. 612 ÷ 4　　　**b.** 805 ÷ 3　　　**c.** 948 ÷ 7　　　**d.** 1476 ÷ 12

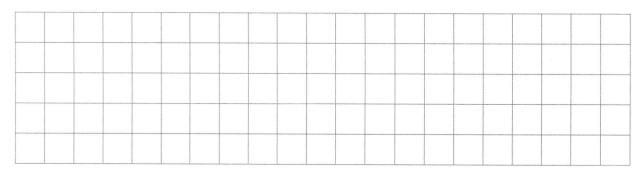

3. Estimate the answer to each of these divisions.

   a. 6345 ÷ 5 = [　　　]　　　　**b.** 3981 ÷ 9 = [　　　]

   c. 4192 ÷ 8 = [　　　]　　　　**d.** 2557 ÷ 12 = [　　　]

4. Now use short division to complete the calculations from Question 3. Take care to lay them out correctly. Give answers with remainders where necessary.

   a. 6345 ÷ 5　　　**b.** 3981 ÷ 9　　　**c.** 4192 ÷ 8　　　**d.** 2557 ÷ 12

1. Write the missing digits in each division.

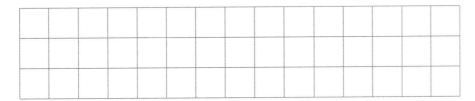

	2	6	7			1	8	2	r1				7	9					□	2	r□
2	5	1□	¹4		3	5	²4	□			□	3	³9	⁴5		1	1	5	⁵7	²3

2. The 575 children in a school are split into four equal houses.

   How many more children are needed to make sure every house has the same number of children?

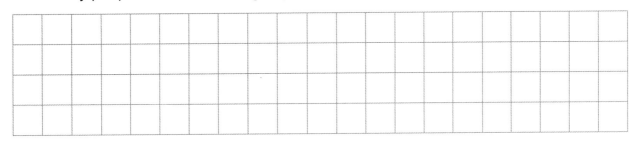

_____ more

3. A group of people win £15,000 on the lottery. They share the win between them equally. Each person receives £1875.

   > **Try divisions using different numbers of people to find the answer.**

   How many people are there in the group?

_____ people

4. One day, a factory makes 3960 tennis balls. They are sorted equally into 12 baskets. The balls in each basket are then sorted equally into six boxes, ready to be sold.

   How many boxes of balls does the factory produce on this day?

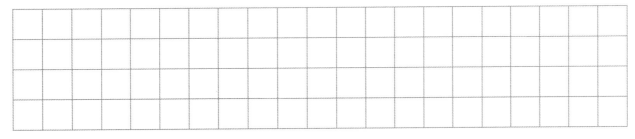

_____ boxes of tennis balls

9 Multiplying and dividing by powers of ten: decimals

⟳ Recap

We use the base 10 number system for whole numbers (1s, 10s, 100s, 1000s, and so on) and for numbers less than 1.

Look at the number 328.56. It has a whole number part of 328, and a decimal part of 0.56.

Hundreds	Tens	Ones		Tenths	Hundredths
$10^2 = 100s$	$10^1 = 10s$	$10^0 = 1s$		$\frac{1}{10^1} = \frac{1}{10} = 0.1$	$\frac{1}{10^2} = \frac{1}{100} = 0.01$
3	2	8	•	5	6

The 5 digit represents five tenths, and the 6 digit represents six hundredths.

We say, "zero point five six".

Decimals are fractions of a whole number. One whole equals ten tenths, and one tenth equals ten hundredths.

Just as with whole numbers, multiplying increases the value of a decimal number and the digits move to the left. Dividing decreases the value of the number, and digits move to the right.

🗎 Learn

When we divide a whole number by a power of 10, some digits may move across the decimal point and become tenths, hundredths, or even thousandths.

For example, $345 \div 10 = 34.5$ $345 \div 100 = 3.45$ $345 \div 1000 = 0.345$.

Or, $230 \div 10 = 23$ $230 \div 100 = 2.3$ $230 \div 1000 = 0.23$.

We can also divide decimals by powers of 10.

For example, $0.3 \div 10 = 0.03$ $0.3 \div 100 = 0.003$.

Or, $2.5 \div 10 = 0.25$ $2.5 \div 100 = 0.025$.

And, of course, we can multiply decimals by powers of 10.

$0.6 \times 10 = 6$ $0.6 \times 100 = 60$ $0.6 \times 1000 = 600$

> Notice how the digits move to the left or the right, making the number smaller when divided by ten, or larger when multiplied by ten.

Look at these different calculations and consider how the value of each digit changes:

$0.048 \times 10 = 0.48$ $48 \div 100 = 0.48$ $9 \div 1000 = 0.009$

$0.375 \times 100 = 37.5$ $0.872 \times 1000 = 872$ $62 \div 10 = 6.2$

Practice

1. Write these numbers using the digits 0–9.

   a. Zero point four six _____

   b. Five point seven zero three _____

   c. Twenty-five and six tenths (as a decimal) _____

   d. Eight hundredths (as a decimal) _____

   e. Two tenths, nine hundredths (as a decimal) _____

2. Complete these multiplications.

   a. $10 \times 3.4 = \boxed{}$

   b. $10 \times 0.6 = \boxed{}$

   c. $10 \times 0.003 = \boxed{}$

   d. $2.4 \times 10 = \boxed{}$

   e. $0.203 \times 100 = \boxed{}$

   f. $1.6 \times 1000 = \boxed{}$

   g. $0.02 \times 1000 = \boxed{}$

   h $0.004 \times 10 = \boxed{}$

   i. $3.7 \times 1000 = \boxed{}$

3. Complete these divisions.

   a. $3 \div 10 = \boxed{}$

   b. $1.2 \div 10 = \boxed{}$

   c. $3.15 \div 10 = \boxed{}$

   d. $862 \div 100 = \boxed{}$

   e. $94 \div 100 = \boxed{}$

   f. $23.6 \div 100 = \boxed{}$

   g. $800 \div 1000 = \boxed{}$

   h. $318 \div 1000 = \boxed{}$

   i. $6 \div 1000 = \boxed{}$

4. Try these harder calculations.

   (Hint: $0.12 \times 20 = 0.12 \times 10 \times 2 = 1.2 \times 2 = 2.4$)

   a. $300 \times 0.02 = \boxed{}$

   b. $25 \div 500 = \boxed{}$

   c. $0.04 \times 5000 = \boxed{}$

   d. $18 \div 9000 = \boxed{}$

   e. $4 \div 800 = \boxed{}$

   f. $200 \div 40{,}000 = \boxed{}$

⚠ Solve problems

1. 1 litre = 1000 millilitres

   How many litres does each of these items hold?

Thimble, 9ml	Egg cup, 25ml	Mug, 300ml	Bottle, 1750ml
_____ litres	_____ litres	_____ litres	_____ litres

2. A single bag of crisps has a mass of 0.056 kilograms. The box the crisps are delivered in has a mass of 0.2 kilograms.

   What is the mass of a box of 100 bags of crisps?

   _____ kg

3. 2000 paper clips have a mass of 850 grams.

   What is the mass of 10 paper clips?

   _____ grams

4. Kevin says, "24 divided by 6000 equals 0.004."

   Explain how he did his calculation.

   _____

   _____

5. A plastic chairs has a mass of 1.63 kilograms.

   A headteacher orders 400 of the chairs.

   What is the total mass of the chairs she orders?

   [   ] kg

10 Scaling and rates, ratio and proportion

Recap

Scale is used for maps, drawings and models.

To calculate the scale upwards, multiply. To calculate the scale downwards, divide.

> On a map with a scale of 1:50, a path is 5cm long. How long is the path in real life?
>
> 5cm on the map represents <u>5 × 50 = 250cm</u> or 2.5m in real life.
>
> A house is drawn at a scale of 1:50. If the house is 10m tall, what size is it in the drawing?
>
> <u>10 ÷ 50 = 0.2m</u> (20cm)

Rates link two different quantities.

> A tap lets water out at two litres every minute. How long will it take to fill a 50-litre barrel? Work out how many lots of two litres there are in 50 litres.
>
> <u>50 ÷ 2 = 25 minutes</u>

Learn

Ratio is something different again – it compares amounts.

> The ratio of girls to boys in a school is 3:2. There are 63 girls. How many boys are there?
>
> <u>63 ÷ 3 = 21</u>   <u>21 × 2 = 42 boys</u>

Proportion deals with fractions and percentages.

> There are six coloured balls in a bag: two are red and four are blue.
>
> $\frac{2}{6}$ are red, $\frac{4}{6}$ are blue. We say that 1 in 3, or $\frac{1}{3}$ are red; and 2 in 3, or $\frac{2}{3}$ are blue.
>
> Notice that we simplify the fractions by dividing by common factors.
>
> Remember, to find a percentage multiply the fraction by 100: e.g. $\frac{1}{4} \times 100 = 25\%$.

1. Class 6 are making a model of their school. They are using a scale of 1:200.

   What length will each of these be for the model? (Remember, there are 100cm in 1 metre.)

   a. Room, 8.6m long, 6m wide: on model: _____cm long, _____cm wide.

   b. Corridor, 25m long, 2.8m wide: on model: _____cm long, _____cm wide.

   c. Hall, 16m long, 9.5m wide: on model: _____cm long, _____cm wide.

   Using measurements from the model, say how long these items are in real life:

   d. Library, 2cm long, 3cm wide: actual: _____m long, _____m wide.

   e. Art cupboard, 1cm long, 1.5cm wide: actual: _____m long, _____m wide.

   f. Music room, 3.5cm long, 4cm wide: actual: _____m long, _____m wide.

2. We pay tax when we earn money. If the **rate** of tax is £1 to pay for every £5 earned, how much tax will be paid on each of these amounts?

   a. £10 earned, tax = £_____   **b.** £50 earned, tax = £_____

   c. £200 earned, tax = £_____   **d.** £560 earned, tax = £_____

   e. £850 earned, tax = £_____   **f.** £24,000 earned, tax = £_____

3. If people enter a park at the rate of six per minute, how many will enter in these times?

   a. 5 minutes: _____ people   **b.** 1 hour: _____ people

4. A zoo has two lions, three giraffes, four elephants, six seals and 18 penguins.

   Write the following ratios in their simplest terms.

   a. penguins : giraffes   **b.** giraffes : seals   **c.** seals : penguins

   _____:_____   _____:_____   _____:_____

5. Paul has four hats and five scarves. How many different hat and scarf combinations can he wear?

   _____

6. Write these proportions as percentages.

   a. 1 in 5 = _____   **b.** 1 in 4 = _____   **c.** 7 in 10 = _____

7. Calculate these proportions of objects.

   a. 1 in 4 of 200 = _____   **b.** 3 in 7 of 21 = _____   **c.** 2 in 3 of 84 = _____

⚠ Solve problems

1. On average, 25% of cars are white.

   In a car park of 1000 cars, how many will not be white?

   _____ cars

2. A large stream flows under a bridge. One winter, a scientist takes measurements, and says it flows at a rate of 250 litres per minute. In summer, after very little rain, the scientist makes new measurements and says it now flows at only 130 litres per minute.

   How many litres per hour **fewer** are flowing in the summer?

   ⬚ litres per hour

3. The ratio of bluebells to daffodils in a field is 20:1.

   Amina and Tina use string to mark a large square. Inside the square they count 17 daffodils.

   If the ratio is correct for their square, how many bluebells will there be?

   _____ bluebells

4. A model of a horse is built at a scale of 1:50.

   The horse is two metres high. What is the height of the model in centimetres?

   _____cm

5. In a school survey, only one in 12 children say that vegetables are their favourite food. Of those children, $\frac{1}{2}$ say they like broccoli best. There are 240 children in the school.

   How many like broccoli best?

   _____ children

6. The ratio of ducks to chickens on a farm is 1:3. Some new chickens arrive and the ratio changes to 2:9. There are 2 ducks.

   How many new chickens arrive?

   _____ chickens

11 Order of operations

↻ Recap

In maths, an operation is a step of a calculation, such as times, square or subtract.

When we have more than one operation in a calculation, we call it multi-step.

For example, for $3 \times 4 + 2$ we must do the multiplication first.

$\underline{3 \times 4 + 2 = 12 + 2 = 14}$ ✓

If we did the addition first, we would get a wrong answer.

$\underline{3 \times 4 + 2 = 3 \times 6 = 18}$ ✗

🗎 Learn

We can use **BIDMAS** to remember the order in which we should do the operations in any multi-step calculation.

Brackets **I**ndices **D**ivision **M**ultiplication
Addition **S**ubtraction

When working just with multiplication and division, work from left to right. Do the same with addition and subtraction: work from left to right.

> **We do whatever calculations are in the brackets first. Then we do any squares or cubes. Next come division and multiplication. Finally, we do any addition and subtraction.**

Look at these examples – they are all correct.

Work through them line by line, saying which operation has been done at each step.

$43 - 30 + 4 - 2$ $13 + 4 - 2$ $17 - 2$ Answer = 15	$(43 - 30) + 4 - 2$ $13 + 4 - 2$ $17 - 2$ Answer = 15	$43 - 30 + (4 - 2)$ $43 - 30 + 2$ $13 + 2$ Answer = 15
$5 \times 12 - 9 \div 3$ $5 \times 12 - 3$ $60 - 3$ Answer = 57	$5 \times (12 - 9) \div 3$ $5 \times 3 \div 3$ 5×1 Answer = 5	$5 \times (12 - 9 \div 3)$ $5 \times (12 - 3)$ 5×9 Answer = 45
$11^2 - 10 \times 7 + 5$ $121 - 10 \times 7 + 5$ $121 - 70 + 5$ $121 - 75$ Answer = 56	$(11^2 - 10) \times (7 + 5)$ $(121 - 10) \times (7 + 5)$ $111 \times (7 + 5)$ 111×12 Answer = 1332	$(11^2 - 10 \times 7) + 5$ $(121 - 10 \times 7) + 5$ $(121 - 70) + 5$ $51 + 5$ Answer = 56

Practice

1. Answer these multi-step calculations using multiplication, division, addition and subtraction.

   Remember, in **BIDMAS**: division and multiplication, then addition and subtraction.

   a. $64 \div 8 + 7 =$ ☐

   b. $3 \times 11 - 25 =$ ☐

   c. $7 + 4 \times 2 =$ ☐

   d. $12 - 60 \div 12 =$ ☐

   e. $23 - 6 \times 3 =$ ☐

   f. $3 \times 7 + 5 \times 4 =$ ☐

   g. $40 \div 5 - 36 \div 6 =$ ☐

   h. $24 \div 3 + 8 \times 6 - 50 =$ ☐

2. Answer these multi-step calculations using multiplication, division and indices.

   Remember, in **BIDMAS**: indices, then division and multiplication

   a. $3^2 \times 2 =$ ☐

   b. $24 \div 2^2 =$ ☐

   c. $10^2 - 12 \times 8 =$ ☐

   d. $11 \times 7 - 8^2 =$ ☐

   e. $4 + 6^2 \div 2 =$ ☐

   f. $(7^2 \times 2) - 4 + 5^2 =$ ☐

   g. $3^2 \times 2^3 - 50 =$ ☐

   h. $27 \div 3^2 + (15 - 8) =$ ☐

3. Answer these multi-step calculations using all operations.

   Remember, in **BIDMAS**: any calculations in brackets come first.

   a. $4 \times (5 - 2) =$ ☐

   b. $(3 + 5) \times (9 - 4) =$ ☐

   c. $20 - 10 \div (2 + 3) =$ ☐

   d. $40 - (6^2 - 3^2) + 50 =$ ☐

   e. $\frac{1}{4} \times 20 - \frac{1}{3} \times 15 =$ ☐

   f. $(21 - 3 \times 2) \times (\frac{1}{2} \times 10) =$ ☐

   g. $3^2 + (41 - 5) \div 4 =$ ☐

   h. $(37 - 4 \times 3) - 5^2 =$ ☐

⚠ Solve problems

1. Add a pair of brackets in this calculation to make it correct.

$$4 + 16 \div 5 - 4 = 0$$

2. Draw lines to connect each calculation to its answer.

| $6 + 7 \times 4 - 1$ | 27 | $(6 + 7) \times 4 - 1$ | 33 |

| $6 + 7 \times (4 - 1)$ | 39 | $(6 + 7) \times (4 - 1)$ | 51 |

3. Jim needs help with this calculation: $52 - 20 + 4 \times 3$.

   Explain to Jim how to do it, and what the answer will be.

   _____

   _____

4. Find the missing number in each calculation.

   a. $20 - \boxed{} \times 2 + 5 = 11$

   b. $4 \times (7 - \boxed{}) - 8 = 0$

   c. $(30 - 8) - \boxed{}^2 + 14 = 20$

   d. $24 \div \boxed{} - 3) \times 5 = 20$

5. One of these calculations does not equal 23. Circle it.

   $3 \times 4 + 4^2 - (15 \div 3)$ $50 - 4 \times 8 + 10 \times \frac{1}{2}$

   $11 \times 3 - (2 + 1) \times 3$ $\frac{1}{2}$ of $20 \times 4 - 17$

12 Written methods: long multiplication

Recap

It's a good idea to look back at Unit 7 Written methods: short multiplication on page 24 before you start this unit. Check the methods you used there: it will make this unit easier.

For a harder multiplication like 43 × 12, we can still use base 10 columns.

	100s	10s	1s
		4	3
×		1	2
		8	6
+	4	3	0
	5	1	6
	1		

We do the calculation like this:

First multiply 43 by 2.

$2 \times 3 = 6$ and $2 \times 4 = 8$

Place a 0 in the **1s** column below the 6.

Now multiply 43 by 1.

$1 \times 3 = 3$ and $1 \times 4 = 4$

Add together 86 and 430.

The answer is 516.

Learn

The same method works for more complicated calculations, such as 596 × 34.

> Work slowly, step by step, checking your work as you go.

Now we can do our written calculation.

	10,000s	1000s	100s	10s	1s
				5	9	6
×					3	4
			2	3₃	8₂	4
		1	7₂	8₁	8	0
		2	0₁	2₁	6	4

First multiply 596 by 4.

$4 \times 6 = 24$ → write 4 in the **1s** column and carry the 2.

$4 \times 9 = 36$, plus 2 is 38 → write 8 in the **10s** column and carry the 3.

$4 \times 5 = 20$, plus 3 is 23 → write 3 in the **100s** column and the 2 in the **1000s** column.

Place a 0 in the 1s column below the 4.

Now multiply 596 by 3.

$3 \times 6 = 18$ → write 8 in the **10s** column and carry the 1.

$3 \times 9 = 27$, plus 1 is 28 → write 8 in the **100s** column and carry the 2.

$3 \times 5 = 15$, plus 2 is 17 → write 7 in the **1000s** column and the 1 in the **10,000s** column.

Finally, add together 2384 and 17,880.

The answer is 20,264.

1. Use long multiplication to work out these.

a. **b.** **c.**

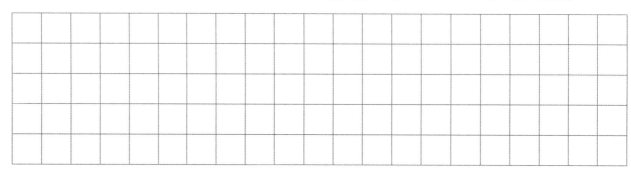

	100s	10s	1s			1000s	100s	10s	1s			1000s	100s	10s	1s
		2	5					5	6					1	2	6
×		1	4		×			2	3		×				1	7

2. Use long multiplication to work out these. Take care to lay them out correctly.

   a. 16 × 25 **b.** 32 × 49 **c.** 55 × 63 **d.** 21 × 215

3. Estimate the answer to each of these multiplications.

   a. 14 × 208 = [ ] **b.** 26 × 287 = [ ]

   c. 43 × 685 = [ ] **d.** 32 × 1271 = [ ]

   > **Tips:**
   > a. Try 15 × 200
   > b. Try 25 × 300
   > c. Try 40 × 700
   > d. Try 30 × 1300
   > **You can use your estimates to check your answers in Question 4.**

4. Now use long multiplication to complete the calculations from Question 3. Take care to lay them out correctly.

   a. 14 × 208 **b.** 26 × 287 **c.** 43 × 685 **d.** 32 × 1271

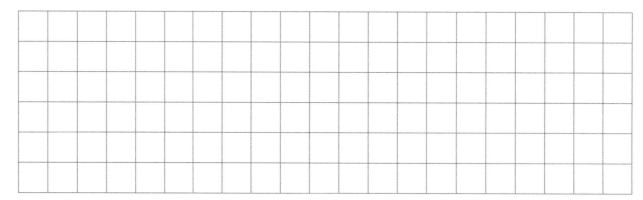

⚠ Solve problems

1. Noah estimates 24 × 363 to be 8700. Use long multiplication to decide whether his estimate was too high or too low, and by how much.

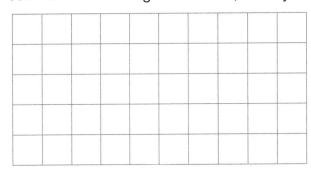

The estimate was _____ too high / low.

2. 542 people each pay £25 to go to the theatre. 58 people get discounts and each pay £10. How much money does the theatre make altogether.

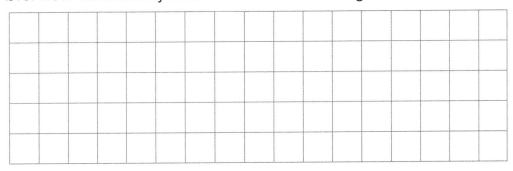

£_____

3. A car factory makes 430 new cars every day. If the factory is open five days a week for 13 weeks, how many cars will they make altogether?

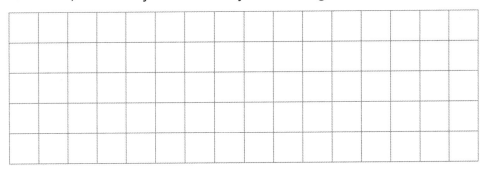

_____ cars

4. A small football stadium holds 3745 people. The stadium is full for every game of a season, and the team played 12 games. How many people were counted going into the stadium altogether that season?

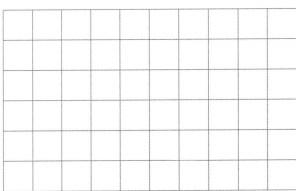

_____ people

13 Written methods: long division

Look back at Unit 8 Written methods: short division (page 27) before you start this unit. Did you understand it all? It will make this work much easier if you do.

We can use short division to divide by a single-digit number, and sometimes by a 2-digit number. For example, we know the 12-times table, so short division by 12 is not too hard.

			2	1	2	r3
1	2	2	5	¹4	²7	

or

			2	1	2	.	2	5
1	2	2	5	¹4	²7	.	³0	⁶0

At the beginning, notice that 12 doesn't go into 2, so instead we start by dividing 12 into 25.

Remember that there are two ways of dealing with the final remainder – we can keep it as a remainder or carry it over the decimal point. We can also convert a remainder or decimal to a fraction.

📄 **Learn**

For harder calculations, we can use long division.

			1	2	3	r1		
2	5	3	0	7	6			
	–	2	5					
			5	7				
		–	5	0		(← 2 × 25)		
				7	6			
		–		7	5	(← 3 × 25)		
					1			

(← 1 × 25)

25 into 3 won't go, so we start by dividing into 30.

25 divides into 30 one time. Write a 1 above the 0.

Write 25 (1 × 25) under the 30 and subtract:
30 – 25 = 5.

Bring down the 7 to make 57.

25 divides into 57 two times. Write a 2 above the 7.

Write 50 (2 × 25) under the 57 and subtract:
57 – 50 = 7.

Bring down the 6 to make 76.

25 divides into 76 three times. Write a 3 above the 6.

Write 75 (3 × 25) under the 76 and subtract:
76 – 75 = 1.

Now we can either write r1 as part of the answer, or continue the long division to get a decimal answer (123.04).

Practice

1. Use long division to work out these. Give answers with remainders where necessary.

a. **b.** **c.**

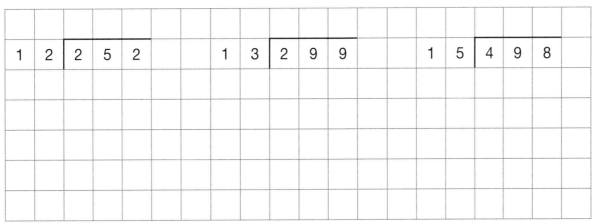

2. Use long division to work out these. Give your answers as decimals.

a. **b.** **c.**

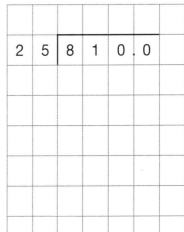

3. Use long division to work out these. Take care to lay them out correctly. Give answers with remainders where necessary.

a. 576 ÷ 13 **b.** 865 ÷ 21 **c.** 1925 ÷ 16

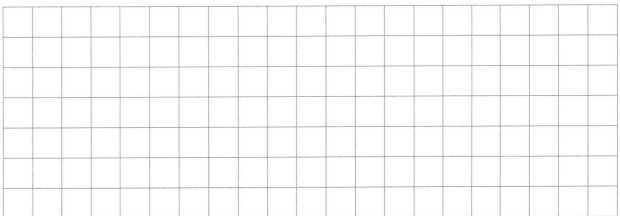

⚠ Solve problems

1. Twelve children share 285 marbles between them. They each get the same number of marbles. How many marbles will be left over?

_____ marbles left over

2. A bread factory makes loaves of bread in 14 batches through the day (one batch of loaves every half hour for seven hours). In a day they make 770 loaves. How many loaves are there in each batch?

_____ loaves in each batch

3. A farmer grows onions. One year, he harvests 5868 onions, and stores them equally in 25 crates. How many spare onions does he have?

_____ onions

4. A teacher has 360 pencils to share equally between 32 children. She immediately says that there will be 8 pencils left over. Explain how she knows this.

_____

_____

Practice test 1 – Arithmetic

There are 20 questions in total. The two "show your method" questions are worth two marks each. All the other questions are worth one mark each.

Try to do the test in one 20-minute sitting. This gives you one minute per question, on average. Remember to read the question and consider if you can use a mental method to solve it before starting any written calculations.

1. $4 \times 9 =$

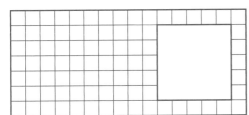

2. $\frac{1}{2}$ of $30 =$

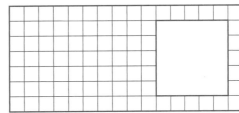

3. $100 \times 27 =$

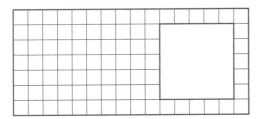

4. $5^2 =$

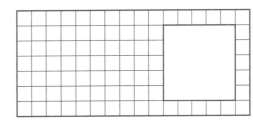

5. $72 \div 8 =$

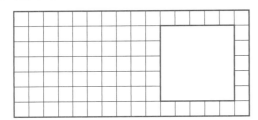

6. $50 \times 60 =$

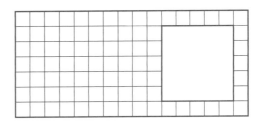

7. 40% of $300 =$

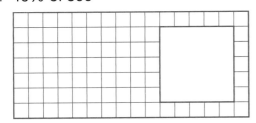

8. $312 \times 3 =$

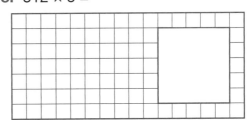

9. $4 + 5 \times 4 =$

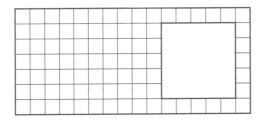

10. $132 \div 6 =$

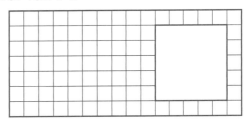

11. $2 \times 5 \times 17 =$

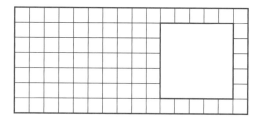

12. $1800 \div 9 =$

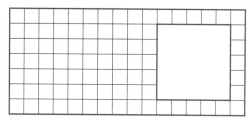

13. $435 \times 5 =$

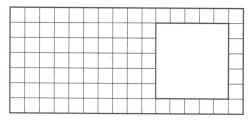

14. $465 \div 1000 =$

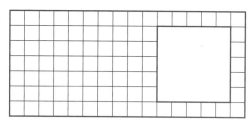

15. Show your method.

		1	8	4
×			3	2

16. $11 \times 415 =$

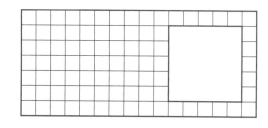

17. $0.7 \times 12 =$

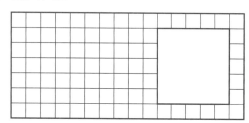

18. $\frac{3}{5}$ of $100 =$

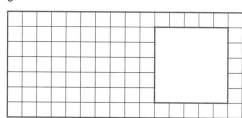

19. $12 \times (32 - 3 \times 7) =$

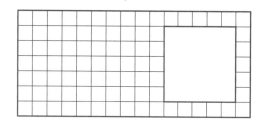

20. Show your method.

2	5	5	7	8

1. Draw lines to match each decimal to its calculation.

| 0.5 | 0.005 | 5 | 0.05 |

| 5 × 0.01 | 5 ÷ 10 | 5 ÷ 1000 | 100 × 0.05 |

2. A cake recipe uses four times more flour than sugar. Shaun uses 125 grams of sugar.

   How much flour does he use?

   _____ grams of flour

3. Solve this mental calculation, and then explain your method.

   $$500 \times 15 = \boxed{}$$

   _____

   _____

4. Complete these number sentences.

   a. $2790 \div \boxed{} = 310$

   b. $460 \div \boxed{} = 23$

5. There are 200 children in a school. The ratio of boys to girls in the school is 2:3.

   How many girls are there altogether?

   _____ girls

6. A farmer has 50 rows of potato plants, with 60 plants in every row.

   If every plant produces four potatoes, how many potatoes will she harvest altogether?

   _____ potatoes

7. Write the missing digits to make this multiplication correct.

		2		1
×			3	4
	1	0	0	4
		5	3	0
		5	3	4

8. Circle the nearest estimate for the calculation 518 × 492.

25,000   20,000   250,000   200,000   2500   2000

9. A delivery van driver has to load the heaviest items first. There are two sets of items. The first set contains nine crates of tinned food that each have a mass of 150kg. The second set contains 20 crates of cereal that each have a mass of 75kg.

Which set of crates should the driver load first?

The set of crates containing _____ should be loaded first

10. Circle the greatest amount of money.

$\frac{1}{7}$ of £8000 $\frac{1}{6}$ of £7000 $\frac{1}{5}$ of £6000 $\frac{1}{4}$ of £5000

11. An audience of 200 is coming to watch a school's Christmas concert. The teachers arrange seats in equal rows. There are 13 seats in each row. Some people, fewer than there are in a full row, have to stand.

Calculate how many rows there are, and how many of the audience will have to stand.

_____ rows, _____ people standing

12. Insert the missing number to make this calculation correct.

$$5^2 - 3 \times (9 - 4) + 15 \div (6 - \boxed{}) = 13$$